To: Jolie
& SAVANNAH

Aunt
From: Kelly

May 2011

Happy JazzFest

A Story for All Ages about the Greatest Festival in the World

Written by Cornell P. Landry • Illustrated by Sean Gautreaux

AMP&RSAND, INC.

Chicago, Illinois

ISBN 978-145070618-6

10 9 8 7 6 5 4 3 2

Design
David Robson, Robson Design

Photography
Scott McCrossen
www.five65.com

Published by
Ampersand, Inc.
1050 N. State Street, Chicago, IL 60610
www.ampersandworks.com

Printed in Canada

To my wife, Christen,
and two wonderful daughters, Bailey and Corinne.

To the millions of JazzFest fans who have attended over the years.

And to those who will make the pilgrimage to New Orleans
for the "Funk, Food and Fun!"

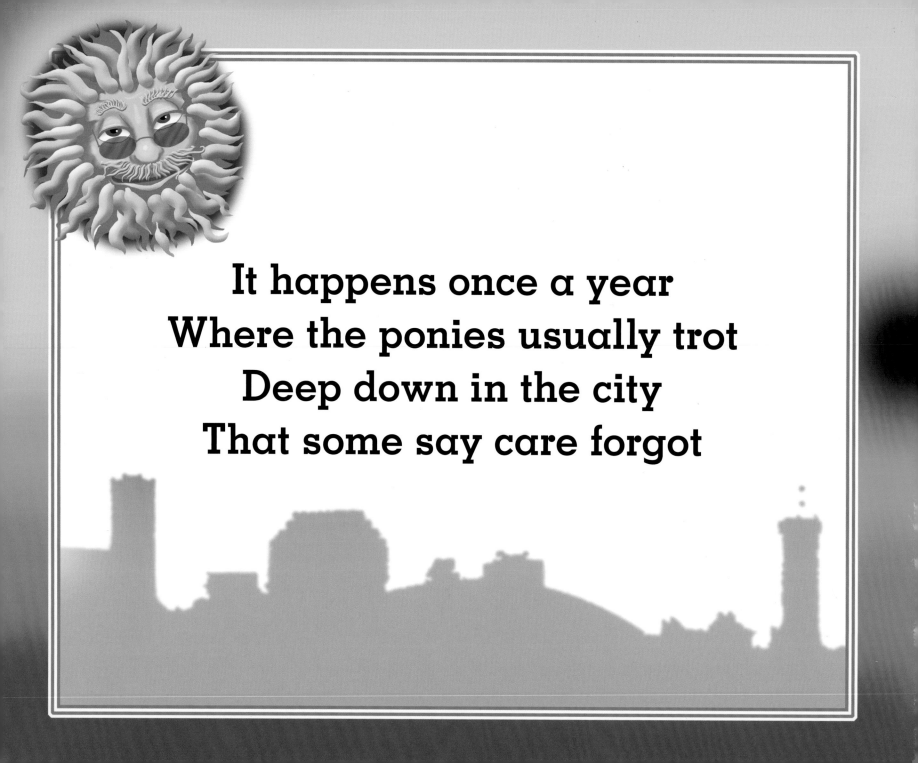

It happens once a year
Where the ponies usually trot
Deep down in the city
That some say care forgot

It's a place to have fun
You can act downright silly
It's right in the heart
Of "Chilly Gentilly"

It's the last weekend in April
And the first weekend in May
It's where all the great bands
And musicians come to play

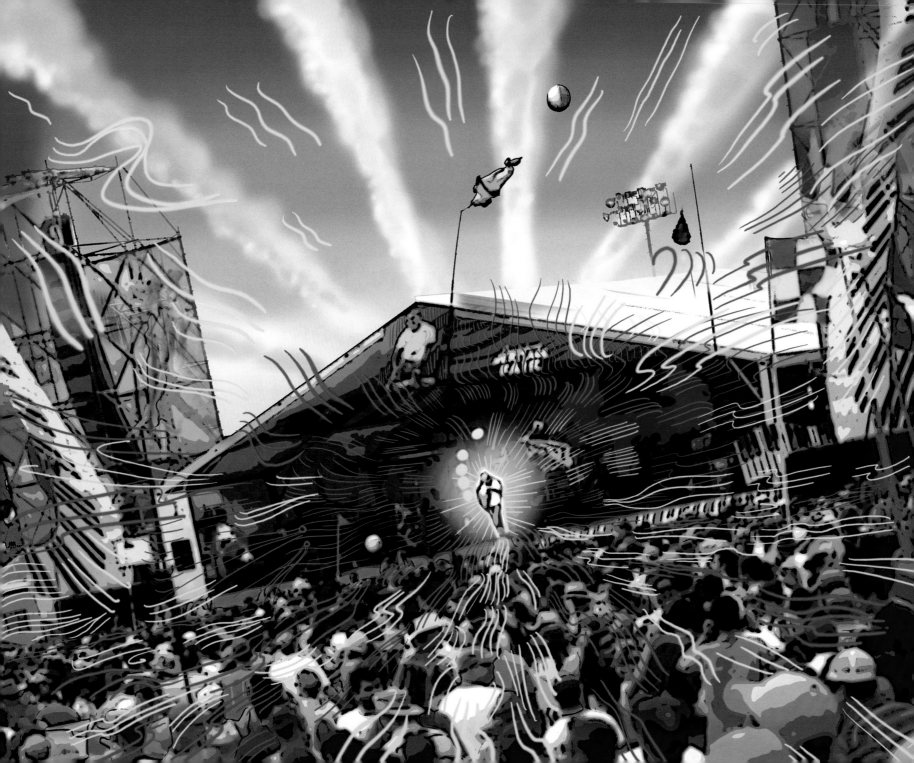

It's a place you will hear
The best of the best
There can only be ONE
New Orleans JazzFest

So unfold your blanket
And open up your chair
You can set up base camp
Right here in Congo Square

Be prepared to dance
To see what's all the rage
When a New Orleans brass band
Gets up on that stage

It's an overload of the senses
Sight, smell and sound
Hop onto the racetrack
And take a lap around

There are arts and crafts
And food booths galore
Take it all in
See what's in store

Around this great Fairground
Maybe you'll find
Big Chief Bo Dollis
Or a New Orleans Second Line

Go to the Blues Tent
Go to the Gospel Tent
If you're lucky you'll catch Mavis
And, what would JazzFest be
without the great Quint Davis?

He's the man with the plan
He's been here from the start
Keep your eyes peeled
For him to fly by in his cart

Seven days are far too short
For an event that's so much fun
It seems when it's almost over
That the Fest has just begun

When the Nevilles take the stage
You know the end's in sight
It's time to take a walk around
To look for a last good bite

Only 90 minutes left
For the Funk, Food and Fun
The Fest comes to an end
When the Neville Brothers are done

Then a lull falls over the crowd
Because a year will have to pass
Before festival-goers
Can walk on infield grass

Seven glorious days
Make us stand up and cheer
HAPPY JazzFest, EVERYBODY
We'll see ya'll again next year!

ACKNOWLEDGMENTS

Gentilly is an old New Orleans neighborhood built on Gentilly Ridge, the high ground of the former banks of Bayou Gentilly. In the 18th Century it was a swamp. The land along Gentilly Ridge was flood-free and a route named Gentilly Road, also known as the Spanish Trail, was formed, giving access to the old part of the city.

Dr. John was born Mac Rebennack on November 21, 1940. In the late 1960s Rebennack changed his name to **Dr. John, the Night Tripper** after the legendary Voo Doo priest of the 1800s. Some of his most famous songs are "Such a Night," "Right Place, Wrong Time" and "Iko Iko."

The first **New Orleans Jazz and Heritage Festival** was held in 1970. According to the official Jazz Fest website, "The Festival celebrates the indigenous music and culture of New Orleans and Louisiana, so the music encompasses every style associated with the city and the state: blues, R&B, gospel, Cajun, zydeco, Afro-Caribbean, folk, Latin, rock, rap, country, bluegrass and everything in between."

Congo Square at Jazz Fest is named for the historical gathering place and trading grounds for African people in colonial New Orleans.

A New Orleans Brass Band – trumpets, trombones, saxophones, sousaphones and percussion – dates back to the late 19th century. These bands play a mix of military and African folk music and usually march at jazz funerals.

The Fairgrounds Race Course is also known as The New Orleans Fairgrounds. The racetrack is owned by Churchill Downs Horse Racing Company, LLC. The Union Race Course was built on the site of The New Orleans Fairgrounds in 1852. It is the oldest race course still in operation in the United States.

In 1964 **Bo Dollis** became Big Chief of the Wild Magnolia Mardi Gras Indian Tribe.

The **Second Line** is rooted in traditional New Orleans Jazz Funerals. Immediate family and friends were in The Main Line. In the Second Line were all the people from the neighborhood who joined in the procession following the burial. They walked down the street dancing and singing in honor of the deceased.

Mavis Staples was a member of the Staples Singers. She was inducted into the Rock and Roll Hall of Fame in 1999 and won the Grammy Lifetime Achievement Award in 2005. Two of her most well known songs are "I'll Take You There" and "Respect Yourself."

Quint Davis is the legendary producer of The New Orleans Jazz and Heritage Festival. He has been a part of the festival since 1970, its very first year.

The Neville Brothers date back to 1976 when Art, Charles, Aaron and Cyril joined together to play for their Uncle Big Chief Jolly's album, "The Wild Tchoupitoulas," named after the famous Mardi Gras Indian Tribe. "The Neville Brothers," their first album, was released in 1978. It is tradition for the Neville Brothers to play the last two sets on the final Sunday of Jazz Fest.